X-MEN®

2008

£6.99

Philadelphia
Birth Place
of the U.S.A
AND IT IS HERE THAT THE ENSLAVEMENT OF THE HUMAN RACE BEGINS--
--ON THIS DAY--
--THE DAY OF THE NEW BROTHERHOOD OF MUTANTS!
X-MEN:
HEROES AND VILLAINS
BY CHUCK AUSTEN & SALVADOR LARROCA
DANNY MIKI INKER
LIQUID! COLORS
VC'S RUS WOOTON LETTERS
STEPHANIE MOORE & SEAN RYAN ASSISTANT EDITORS
MIKE MARTS EDITOR
JOE QUESADA EDITOR IN CHIEF
DAN BUCKLEY PUBLISHER

I AM EXODUS, AND I AM THE POWER AND THE WAY--
--FIRST DISCIPLE TO MAGNETO, HERE TO ENSURE HIS GOAL--HIS DREAM--THAT THE END OF HUMAN TYRANNY--
--SHALL BE FULFILLED.
BLAH BLAH BLAH.
AND I AM HAVOK, THE BETTER POWER AND THE BIGGER WAY--
--LEADER OF THE X-MEN--DISCIPLE TO XAVIER--HERE TO MAKE CERTAIN HIS GOAL AND HIS DREAM ARE FULFILLED--
--BY KICKING--
GET 'IM, ALEX.
--YOUR--

UNNF!
SKREEEEEEEM

SABRETOOTH! LONG TIME NO SEE!
CAN'T I GO ANYWHERE WITHOUT RUNNIN' INTO YOU, RUNT?!
SLASH
NO.
AVALANCHE--?
HHLLK!
HEY, ROGUE!
WANNA SHAKE THINGS UP, FOR OLD TIME'S SAKE?
HNGAHNGA HNGA--
TOO BAD YA DON'T HANG WITH THE BROTHERHOOD ANYMORE, BABE...
...THEN I WOULDN'T HAVE TO--
URKK!
CHUD!

WOULDN'T HAVE TO *WHAT,* AVALANCHE?
FORGET THE FACT THAT I CAN *SIPHON OFF* OTHER MUTANTS' POWERS...?
LIKE THOSE OF MY DEAR TEAMMATE *POLARIS?*
CHUO
"BABE."
LOSER.
SLAP
AND HERE I THOUGHT YOU MIGHT NEED *HELP,* ROGUE.
SILLY ME.

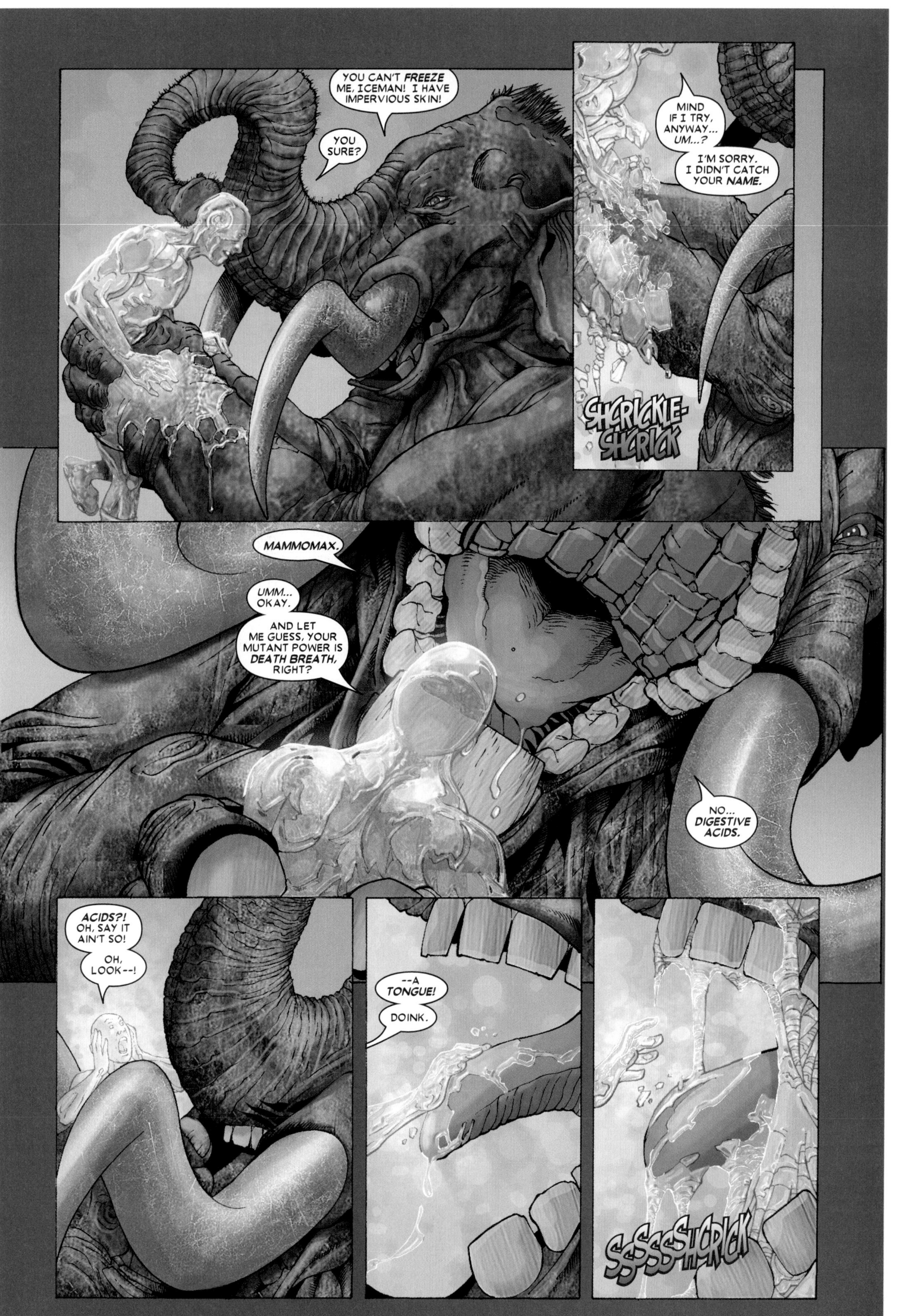
YOU CAN'T FREEZE ME, ICEMAN! I HAVE IMPERVIOUS SKIN!
YOU SURE?
MIND IF I TRY, ANYWAY... UM...?
I'M SORRY. I DIDN'T CATCH YOUR NAME.
SHCRICKLE-SHCRICK
MAMMOMAX.
UMM... OKAY.
AND LET ME GUESS, YOUR MUTANT POWER IS DEATH BREATH, RIGHT?
NO... DIGESTIVE ACIDS.
ACIDS?! OH, SAY IT AIN'T SO!
OH, LOOK--!
--A TONGUE!
DOINK.
SSSSSHCRICK

GUESS YOU'RE NOT AS IMPERVIOUS ON THE *INSIDE,* HUNH?
BET *YOU* FEEL PRETTY STUPID RIGHT ABOUT NOW.
GOING SOMEWHERE, HUMANS?!
OUR INAUGURAL ATTACK WOULDN'T BE VERY *EFFECTIVE* WITHOUT *VICTIMS.*
PETER, HE'S GOING TO KILL US!
LET ME HELP YA OUT HERE, FOLKS.
NOCTURNE, WHAT ARE YOU *DOING?!*
OH! SORRY, TOM! WAS I *NOT* SUPPOSED TO DO THIS?!

NOW *RUN*. GET AWAY, QUICKLY.
YOU'RE SUPPOSED TO BE ON *OUR* SIDE, YOUNG LADY.
BOOOSH
THWIP
SHLIP
THWICK
OH YEAH. SORRY.
MAYBE SHE'S LOOKING FOR MORE *INTELLIGENT* COMPANIONSHIP, TOM?
AS OPPOSED TO *YOU*--
--HAVOK--
THWICK
KLIP
--WHO HAS DONE SOMETHING VERY, VERY *STUPID?*
FLIP
CHRACK

X-MEN! EVERYBODY DOWN!
FAAAASH
SSSSSSSSSSS
UMM...

...WOW. NICE WORK, ALEX.
I BET PHILADELPHIA IS *REEEEALLY* GLAD THE X-MEN SHOWED UP.

UNH NOT ONE O' MY *BETTER DAYS...*
FOR *ANY* OF US, LOGAN.
BUT ESPECIALLY *ALEX,* WHO UNBALANCED THE REST OF US LONG ENOUGH FOR THIS NEW *"BROTHERHOOD"* TO GET *AWAY--*

--AND BEFORE WE COULD LEARN WHAT THEIR *ANGLE* IS.
I'LL ACCEPT THE BLAME FOR THEM GETTING AWAY, BUT WE *WILL* LEARN WHAT THEIR ANGLE IS...

"...THAT I CAN *PROMISE* YOU."
THE XAVIER INSTITUTE FOR HIGHER LEARNING
HEY, ANYONE SEEN *CAIN* LATELY?
YOU KNOW-- *"JUGGERNAUT"?*
NOT SINCE LAST NIGHT, SAMMY.

THAT'S WHAT I WANNA KNOW, FISH BOY! WHERE'S JUGGERNAUT?!
WE JUST FOUGHT AGAINST SOME OF HIS OLD BUDDIES, AND WE COULDA USED HIM--
BOBBY, CALM DOWN.
CAIN ISN'T REQUIRED TO COME ALONG ON MISSIONS IF HE--
THAT'S WRONG AND YOU KNOW IT, ALEX!
IT'S PART OF HIS PAROLE AGREEMENT THAT HE BE AVAILABLE TO THIS TEAM AND HAVE HIS PRESENCE ACCOUNTED FOR--
--AT-- ALL-- TIMES!
BOBBY, LISTEN--
NO, I WILL NOT LISTEN.
IF CAIN CAN'T BE ACCOUNTED FOR IN THE NEXT FIVE MINUTES--I REPORT HIM TO THE AUTHORITIES!
ALEX!
HEY, CARTER!
HOW'S MY LITTLE MAN?!
GOOD!
BORED WITHOUT YOU.
OH, BROTHER.
THERE YOU ARE, SAMMY! I'VE BEEN LOOKING ALL OVER FOR YOU.
GET LOST, MOM. I'M LOOKING FOR CAIN!

MEANWHILE...
SOMEONE TIPPED THEM OFF!
NOCTURNE'S THE ONLY ONE WE KNOW NOTHING ABOUT! NO ONE ELSE COULD HAVE DONE IT!
NOCTURNE IS FROM ANOTHER DIMENSION, CREED, AND HAS NEVER LEFT MY SIDE SINCE I BROUGHT HER HERE.
AND IF-- AS YOU SAY-- NO ONE ELSE COULD HAVE--
--THEN THERE MUST BE ANOTHER EXPLANATION AS TO HOW THE X-MEN LEARNED OF OUR PLANS.
WELL THEN, MAYBE NOW YOU SEE THE VALUE OF MY PLAN TO ATTACK THEM IN THEIR HOME!
I DO, INDEED, TOM. WE MUST REMOVE THE POTENTIAL THREAT.
BUT THEIR INSTITUTE IS TOO WELL GUARDED. HOW DO WE ATTACK THEM IN THEIR OWN FORTRESS WITHOUT AN EDGE OF SOME KIND?
AH, BUT THAT'S THE BEAUTY OF WORKING WITH ME, EXODUS.
I'VE HAD A PLAN IN MOTION TO GIVE US AN EDGE FOR QUITE SOME TIME NOW...

Continued on page 20

SELECT PROFILE

X-MEN

The X-Men were founded by Professor Charles Xavier to promote his ideals of a peaceful human/mutant coexistence

CLICK ICON BELOW

JUGGERNAUT

WOLVERINE

JUGGERNAUT

Action image >>>

BACKGROUND >>>

Cain Marko is Charles Xavier's stepbrother.

As an adult, Cain discovered an ancient temple and the Crimson Gem of Cyttorak. Cain took the gem and was instantly transformed into the living powerhouse known as the Juggernaut. Cain decided to use his powers to kill Xavier, however, the X-Men thwarted every attempt.

Cain then formed a criminal partnership with the mutant mercenary Black Tom Cassidy.

Many years later, Cain reconcilled his differences with Xavier and joined the X-Men, where he made friends with a young mutant Samuel (Sammy) Pare.

MUTANT POWERS

Superhuman Strength (able to press over 100 tonnes), Invulnerable to injury, Forcefield

WOLVERINE

Action image >>>

Action image >>>

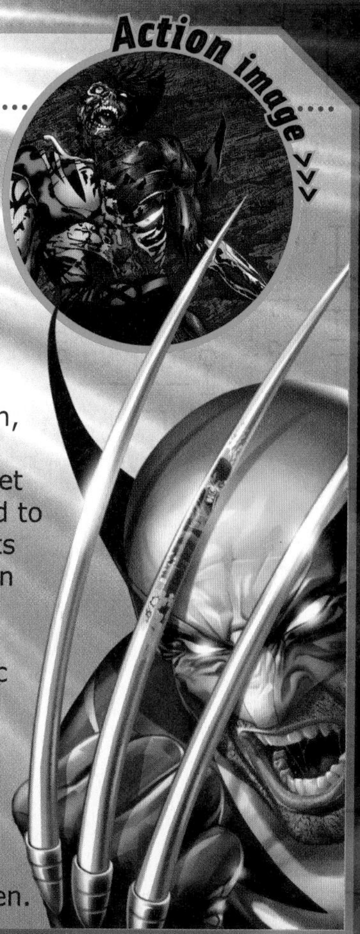

BACKGROUND >>>

Little is known of Wolverine's origin, other than he had volunteered for the Weapon X program, a top secret US government operation designed to create super soldiers. The scientists of Weapon X laced Logan's skeleton with the indestructible metal, adamantium, and they erased his memories. However, his animalistic nature was too strong and he escaped. He joined Canada's top-secret Department H where he was code-named Wolverine. It was whilst at Department H that Wolverine was recruited by Professor X and he joined the X-Men.

MUTANT POWERS

Adamantium Skeleton, Claws, Healing Factor (allowing Wolverine to recover from almost any wound), Enhanced Senses

SELECT PROFILE

>>>>CEREBRO FILES<<<<

CLICK ICON BELOW

HAVOK

ICEMAN

ROGUE

HAVOK

BACKGROUND >>>

Alex is the brother of Scott (Cyclops) Summers. Alex discovered his mutant powers when he was abducted by Ahmet Abdol (the Living Pharoah) in order to unleash his powers and transform into the Living Monolith. Fortunately, the Living Monolith was defeated by the X-Men and Alex was rescued. Soon after, the X-Men rescued Alex from the mutant hunting Sentinels and afterward he joined the X-Men. He has since proven to be a valuable member of the team.

MUTANT POWERS

Plasma Generation (used to create blasts of super-heated plasma), Immune to Cyclops' Optic Blasts

ICEMAN

BACKGROUND >>>

Robert (Bobby) Drake's mutant power to create ice was discovered while in his early teens. A bully named Rocky Beasely and his friends attacked Bobby and his then-girlfriend, Judy Harmon, he panicked and temporarily encased Rocky in ice. Believing the boy to be a menace, the townspeople organised a lynch mob. Fortunately, Bobby was rescued by Professor Charles Xavier and the X-Men. Xavier then offered Bobby a place on the X-Men.

MUTANT POWERS

Ice Generation, Create Ice Slides and blasts, Generates ice to increase his size and strength

ROGUE

BACKGROUND >>>

Anna Marie first learned of her powers during her early teens when she kissed her boyfriend Cody Robbins and absorbed his memories, causing him to fall into a coma. Assuming the name Rogue, she ran away from home and joined Mystique's Brotherhood of Evil Mutants. Not long after, Rogue found she was struggling to cope with her powers and turned to the X-Men and Professor X for help. Despite initial distrust, Rogue has proven herself to be a valued member of the team and is currently romantically involved with Gambit.

MUTANT POWERS

Power Absorption, Strength (able to press approxiamately 50 tonnes) and Endurance, Flight (150 mph), Resistance to Telepathy

X-MEN

The X-Men were founded by Professor Charles Xavier to promote his ideals of a peaceful human/mutant coexistence

GAMBIT

BACKGROUND >>>

Remy Etienne LeBeau was orphaned as a child and adopted by Jean-Luc LeBeau, the head of the New Orleans Thieves' Guild. As a young adult, and now calling himself Gambit, Remy traveled the world as a master thief. Eventually, Gambit encountered Storm and the X-Men and after helping them on several missions he joined the team, where he has since proven himself to be an invaluable member. Gambit is romantically involved with Rogue.

Action image >>>

MUTANT POWERS

Bio-Kinetic Charging, Enhanced Agility, Telepathic Shield, Hypnotic Charm

XORN

BACKGROUND >>>

The Xorn brothers' mutant powers manifested as tiny stars inside their heads that destroyed everything around them. In order to protect the countryside, the Chinese Communist government separated the brothers and incarcerated them. After many years, Kuan-Yin was rescued by the X-Men and he joined their ranks. It was later revealed, however, that Kuan-Yin was in fact a duplicate of Magneto. Fortunately, the X-Men defeated him. Later, the X-Men returned to China and rescued Shen and brought him back to the Xavier Institute.

SHEN XORN

KUAN-YIN XORN

MUTANT POWERS

Energy Generation and Manipulation, Healing, Telepathy, Self Sustenance

GAMBIT

XORN

POLARIS

BACKGROUND >>>

Lorna Dane's mutant powers first manifested when the villain, Mesmero used a Genetic Stimulator to unleash her latent powers. He used his hypnotic powers to control the young mutant. Fortunately, Lorna was rescued by the X-Men.

Soon after, Lorna joined the X-Men in order to learn how to control her powers and assumed the codename Polaris, however, she has always been a reluctant hero.

MUTANT POWERS

Magnetic Manipulation (used to create powerful magnetic blasts, generate force fields and fly)

POLARIS

CLICK ICON ABOVE

SELECT PROFILE

Continued from page 16

THIS DOOR IS OTHERWISE UNPROTECTED.
OUR NEW BROTHERHOOD OF MUTANTS CAN KILL THEM ALL BEFORE THEY EVEN KNOW WE'VE--
NOCTURNE?
WHERE ARE YOU GOING?
NOWHERE, I'M JUST...
...I'M JUST GETTING UNCOMFORTABLE ON THAT--
HEY, I KNOW YOU.
YOU'RE NOT ONE OF US...
YOU'RE THAT EXILES HERO-LADY FROM THE OTHER DIMENSION, AND I--
NO!
NOOO!

AAH!!
SOMEBODY HELP ME!
SKRASH
CAIN CAN BE RATHER BRUTAL WHEN NECESSARY.
SKEESH
BASH
SKRASH
INDEED.
WHAT WERE YOU SAYING TO HER, JUGGY?
MY ENHANCED HEARING PICKED UP SOMETHING...
I...I WAS JUST SAYING I WISHED WE HAD MORE TIME...

...SO WE COULD HAVE HAD MORE *FUN.*
YOU'RE A *PIG...*
...CAIN.
SAMMY, NO...
YOU *MISERABLE, STINKING* PIECE OF *GARBAGE...*

HEY, ALEX. SAMMY WANTED ME TO--
JUGGERNAUT'S GONE, ALEX!

UMM...MR. SUMMERS?
HE'S NOWHERE IN THE BUILDING, AND NOWHERE ON THE GROUNDS!
NO ONE'S SEEN HIM SINCE WHO KNOWS WHEN.
BOBBY, YOU HAVE TO RELAX ABOUT THIS. I'M TELLING YOU, WE DON'T HAVE TO WORRY ABOUT--

YEAH, YOU KEEP TELLING ME. YOU KEEP TELLING ME. BUT NOW I'M TELLING YOU!
JUGGERNAUT'S GOING TO TURN ON US AND YOU'VE SHOWN HIM ALL OUR SECRETS!
BOBBY, HE'S NOT GOING TO TURN ON US. WE'LL FIND HIM--

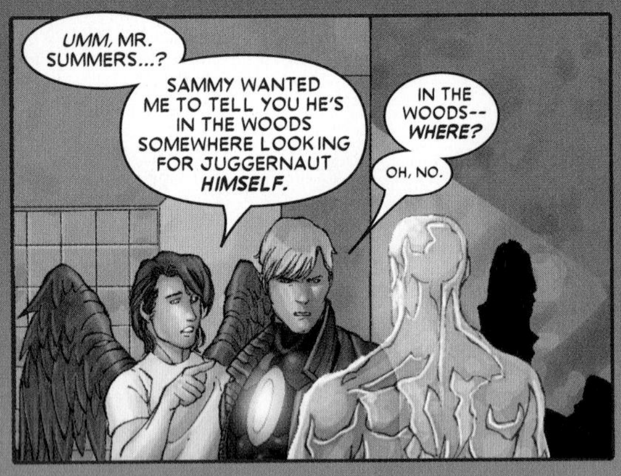
UMM, MR. SUMMERS...?
SAMMY WANTED ME TO TELL YOU HE'S IN THE WOODS SOMEWHERE LOOKING FOR JUGGERNAUT HIMSELF.
IN THE WOODS-- WHERE?
OH, NO.

A-AT THE EDGE OF THE GROUNDS, NEAR THAT STRANGE TREE WE SAW!
WHAT STRANGE TREE?
SAMMY THOUGHT JUGGERNAUT MIGHT HAVE GONE IN TO LOOK FOR A "BLACK..."
...I DON'T KNOW, BLACK SOMEBODY-OR-OTHER.

BLACK TOM?
I KNEW IT!

DON'T JUST STAND THERE, BOBBY--
COME ON!
TOLD YA SO.

I CAN'T BELIEVE I EVER BOUGHT INTO YOUR ACT!
WHAT AN IDIOT I WAS! YOU MUSTA BEEN LAUGHING YOURSELF SICK!
KID, YOU-- YOU AIN'T SUPPOSED TO BE HERE.
GET OUTTA HERE, OKAY? THIS--
I KNOW I WAS LAUGHING MYSELF SILLY, BOY.
WATCHING YOU TWO ALL THIS TIME, PLAYING CATCH-- TALKING ABOUT GIRLS...
IT WAS SO BRILLIANTLY--
--DOMESTIC!
THOO!
YOU DISGUST ME, CAIN.
AND TO THINK I ALWAYS WONDERED IF I MIGHT BE LIKE YOU. A BAD GUY. SOMEONE WHO COULD HURT OTHERS AND LIKE IT.
FEEL GOOD ABOUT IT.
WELL, I'M NOT. I'M A GOOD GUY. SOMEONE WHO REALLY BELIEVES IN XAVIER'S DREAM.
A HERO.

I'M AN X-MAN--
--AND YOU'RE NOT GETTING PAST ME.
OH, PLEASE--
THWIP
SHLICK
KWIP
CRACK
SAMMY!
SAMMY!
SHNAP

SAMMY...
YOU--
--ARE--
--DEAD!

THAT SCREAM CAME FROM OVER THERE!
POLARIS! LOGAN!
I'M HALFWAY THERE, ALEX.
AND I GOT A SCENT.
JAY! GET BACK TO THE SCHOOL! IT'S NOT SAFE OUT HERE!
AND TELL SCOTT TO LOCK DOWN THE MANSION, AND GET THE STUDENTS TO SAFETY--CODE RED!
ALEX. A LIFE HAS BEEN LOST.
THE SPIRIT HAS CROSSED OVER. BUT I DON'T KNOW WHOSE.
CAN YOU GET THEM BACK, XORN?
I AM SORRY, ALEX. BUT THAT KIND OF HEALING IS BEYOND ME--
"--BEYOND ANYONE."
KRUNK!

NOOOOOOOOO!
YOU'RE MAKING ENOUGH NOISE TO WAKE THE DEAD, JUGGERNAUT.
I HAVE TO ASSUME OUR ELEMENT OF SURPRISE IS LOST.
THWICK
CREAK
RRRRK
OR DID WE EVER TRULY HAVE IT?
SO YOU NEVER EVEN ONCE THOUGHT THAT JUGGERNAUT WAS PLAYING US FOR FOOLS?!
I...
...NO, BOBBY. I DIDN'T.

THEN YOU'RE EVEN STUPIDER THAN I THOUGHT.
YOU THINK SCOTT WOULDA LET THIS SLIDE THROUGH?
BOBBY, CAIN HAD SCOTT'S TRUST! HE HAD XAVIER'S!
I GUESS... I GUESS WE WERE JUST TOO TRUSTING.
BUT RIGHT NOW OUR PRIORITY IS LOCATING SAMMY AND THIS NEW BROTHERHOOD, NOT--
UH, ALEX...?
THWOOM

...I THINK WE FOUND THEM...
X-MEN.
AS I EXPECTED...
IF YOU EXPECTED IT--
--THEN WHY WEREN'T YOU BETTER--
--PREPARED...?
FWEEEEN
SKROOM!

WE...WE'RE BEING TORN APART...
NO!
SHBOOM
RMMMBOOOM
RMMMMM

BEEESH
SLAASH
BACK AWAY, SABRETOOTH!
LET ME FINISH THIS!
KRRRMMBBBLLL
CLAP!

EXCELLENT.
PERHAPS THIS PLAN IS NOT THE FAILURE I FEARED IT HAD BECOME.
NOW.
LET'S GO KILL THE REST OF THE X-MEN.

THE XAVIER INSTITUTE FOR HIGHER LEARNING
ANNIE?
ANNIE, CAN YOU TELL ME IF THIS CARD IS GLOWING OR NOT?
HELLOOOO?
ANNIE?
HAD ENOUGH O' THIS REHAB BUSINESS.
ALL RIGHT, IF YOU'RE NOT HERE TO TELL ME NOT TO, THEN MY BANDAGES CAN COME--
WHOA--
--NOW WHAT IS DIS?

LOOK AT 'EM ALL. FISH IN A BARREL.
NO IDEA THE NEW BROTHERHOOD OF MUTANTS IS AT THEIR DOORSTEP.
SO WHERE DO WE START, EXODUS?
DOES IT REALLY MATTER TO YOU, CREED? ISN'T THIS JUST ANOTHER PAYCHECK FOR ONE SUCH AS YOURSELF?
PRETTY MUCH.
WELL TO ME, THESE ARE THE MONSTERS WHO KILLED OUR LORD AND MASTER, MAGNETO.
THEY ALL DIE.
START WHEREVER YOU PLEASE.

HEY!
IS ANYONE HERE?!
SCHOOL O' TWO HUNDRED STUDENTS AN' CAN'T FIND A BLASTED ONE--
YES?
STOP SHOUTING PLEASE, I'M--
MR. LeBEAU?
LISTEN, GIRL--IT'S MINDEE, RIGHT?
I'M BLIND, AND I NEED YOU TO LOOK OUTSIDE AND TELL ME IF YOU SEE SOMETHING!
IS IT SOMETHING SO URGENT IT CAN'T WAIT A MINUTE OR TWO, WHILE I--
NOW!
FINE. NOT LIKE ANYTHING CAN GET THROUGH MISS FROST'S PSYCHIC DEFENSES, ANYWAY...
WHAT HAPPENED? YOU HEAR A PUPPY GROWL?
SMELL A SKUNK, PERHAPS?
NOTHIN' LIKE DAT, NO. I--I HAD DIS VISION, AND--

KEEEESH
AAAAAH!

KASH
TINK
TIINK
CLINK

YOU ALL RIGHT?!
WHAT WAS THAT CRASH?!
OOOOH, I SMELL TWO MORE VICTIMS... AND ONE'S THE CAJUN!
CREED?
I'LL USE MY TELEPATHY AND BE YOUR EYES' MR' LEBEAU!

HAAAAAH!
FLING!

KEESHOOOOOOM

THAT WORKED RATHER WELL.
AN' I GOT PLENTY MORE CARDS TO PLAY, MINDEE.
RRRMMMMMMMMM
AAH!
IT'S AVALANCHE!
YOU ARE DEAD, LI'L GIRL, YOU ARE SOOO--
FWWWWSHH!
YOU GONNA FINISH THAT SENTENCE, SABRETOOTH?
OR BETTER YET, MAYBE I'LL JUST KILL THE--
SABRETOOTH?
I THINK HE GOT SMART AND RAN, MISTER.
AAAAH!
TOO LATE FOR YOU TO DO THE SAME.

HELLO, SABRETOOTH-- REMEMBER ME?
I'M THE ONE WITH SUPERSPEED, AND YOU'RE THE ONE WITH THE MUTANT HEALING POWER.
LET'S PUT BOTH TO THE TEST, SHALL WE?
CHEESH
OR...
...WE CAN WAIT TILL YOU WAKE UP.
NOW...
...WHERE ARE THE X-MEN?

Continued on page 44

>>>>CEREBRO FILES<<<<

CLICK ICON BELOW

EXODUS

BLACK TOM

AVALANCHE

EXODUS

BACKGROUND >>>

Bennet Du Paris was a 12th Century Crusader who encountered the immortal mutant warlord Apocalypse, who unleashed his latent mutant powers and created Exodus. Apocalypse, however, imprisoned Exodus in a state of suspended animation where he remained for centuries until he was freed by Magneto. Exodus became an ardent follower of Magneto and after the Master of Magnetism's apparent demise formed a new Brotherhood of Mutants.

MUTANT POWERS

Telekinesis, Telepathy, Teleportation, Energy Vampire, Resurrection

BLACK TOM

BACKGROUND >>>

Thomas Samuel Eamon Cassidy is the cousin of Sean Cassidy, better known as the X-Man Banshee. After Tom discovered that he had the mutant ability to channel blasts of energy through his shillelagh (an Irish club) he assumed the name Black Tom and embarked upon a life of crime. He formed a criminal partnership with Juggernaut and often fought the X-Men.
Years later, Black Tom had a wood-like substance grafted to his body. Due to a genetic virus, Tom's body became completely composed of plant matter.

MUTANT POWERS

Plant Form, Plant Manipulation (allowing total control over all plant life)

AVALANCHE

BACKGROUND >>>

Little is known of the early years of Dominic Szilard Janos Petros, before he was recruited by Mystique for the second incarnation of the Brotherhood of Evil Mutants. After being defeated by the X-Men, Avalanche left the Brotherhood and attempted to make a criminal career of his own. However, the Hulk defeated him. Soon after, he received a pardon by the US government in return for performing missions as part of Freedom Force. Recently, this team was disbanded.

MUTANT POWERS

Vibration Waves (generating small, but devastating earthquakes)

BROTHERHOOD OF MUTANTS

The Brotherhood were orginally founded by Magneto to further his cause of mutant supremacy.

SABRETOOTH

BACKGROUND >>>

Little is known of Victor Creed's early years, however, it is understood that during the 1960s, Sabretooth was as a member of Team X, a covert military unit run by the United States' Central Intelligence Agency - part of the shadowy Weapon X program. Wolverine was also an operative of Team X. After Sabretooth murdered a female agent that Team X had been sent to rescue an intense hatred for each other developed that has lasted to this day.

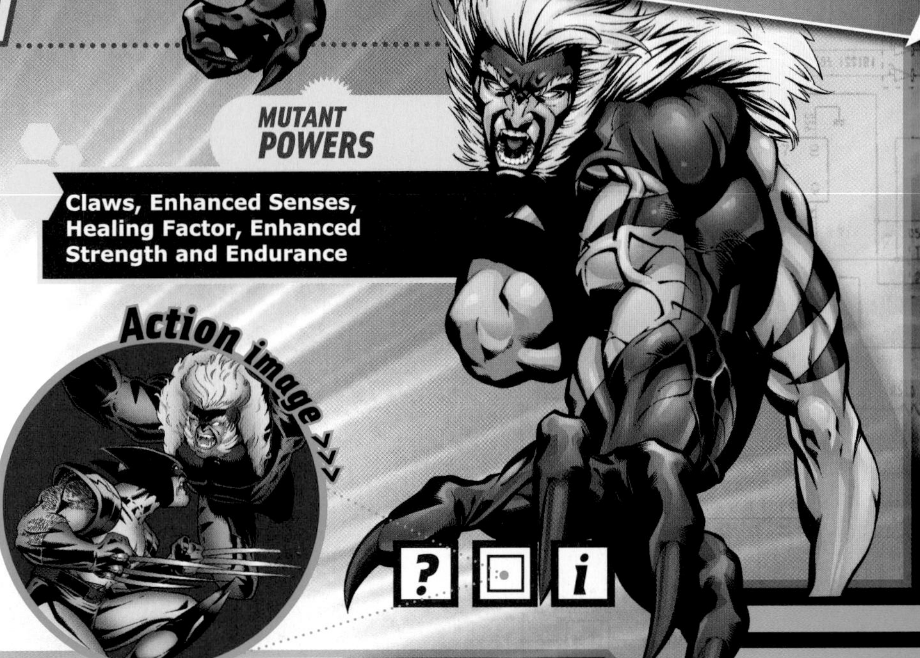

MUTANT POWERS

Claws, Enhanced Senses, Healing Factor, Enhanced Strength and Endurance

Action image >>>

NOCTURNE

BACKGROUND >>>

Talia Josephine (TJ) Wagner hails from another dimension where she is the daughter of Nightcrawler and the Scarlet Witch of the Avengers.

One night she was informed by the powerful alien known as the Timebroker that she had become 'unhinged' in time. Consequently she joined the team of outcasts from other realities known as the Exiles. During a mission to the Marvel Universe, Nocturne was left behind and she infiltrated Exodus's new Brotherhood of Mutants.

MUTANT POWERS

Possession, Hex Bolts, Enhanced Agility, Limited Telepathy

MAMMOMAX

BACKGROUND >>>

Little is known about the origins of Maximus Jensen, better known as the elephantine powerhouse Mammomax, other than he is a willing follower of Exodus and his new Brotherhood of Mutants.

MUTANT POWERS

Superhuman Strength (able to press around 75 tonnes) and Endurance, Impervious Hide, Corrosive Stomach Acids

SABRETOOTH

NOCTURNE

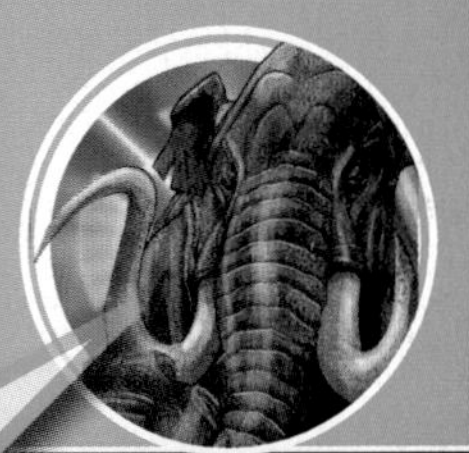

MAMMOMAX

CLICK ICON ABOVE

SELECT PROFILE

Continued from page 41

QUITE IMPRESSIVE, TOM. QUITE IMPRESSIVE.
BASH
KEESH
BOOM
MINDEE, CAN'T YOUR MENTAL POWERS STOP THESE GUYS?
NO! EXODUS IS PSYCHICALLY SHIELDED AND BLACK TOM'S MIND IS INACCESSIBLE TO ME, SO--
SHBOOM
WHAT'S HAPPENING?!
WHAT'S GOING ON?!
DON'T WORRY! THERE'S NOTHING TO WORRY ABOUT!
EVERYTHING'S... FINE.

ROGUE, ROGUE, ROGUE...
....ABSORBED WOLVERINE'S POWERS, I SEE?

SO IF I SHATTER YOU TO BITS, WILL HIS HEALING POWER PUT YOU BACK TOGETHER PROPERLY?
OR WILL IT PUT YOU BACK TOGETHER TO LOOK LIKE WOLVERINE?
YOU AIN'T GOT THE MANHOOD TO DO IT, TOM!
OH, I BEG TO DIFFER.
TRUST ME. THIS KILLING METHOD HAS BEEN ROAD-TESTED.
AAAAAHH!!

YOU OKAY, XORN?
I DON'T BREATHE, SO YES, I'M FINE.
I WAS USING THE TIME TO MEDITATE.
GOOD FOR YOU.
HERE YOU ALL ARE!
THE SCHOOL'S UNDER ATTACK! I'VE BEEN CRISSCROSSING THE FOREST LOOKING FOR--
UNDER ATTACK?! WHY AREN'T YOU THERE, HELPING?!
WHY AREN'T YOU?
AT LEAST I HAVE AN EXCUSE. I AM NOT OFFICIALLY ON AN "X TEAM."
THEY'VE KILLED SAMMY!
WELL, YOU ARE NOW, BUD. WE'LL TAKE ANYONE WHO'S WILLING.
WHAT?
ARE YOU SERIOUS?
CAIN?
DON'T SAY NOTHIN'. JUST LEAD.
I INTEND TO.
LET'S PUT AN END TO THESE KILLERS, NO MATTER WHAT IT TAKES.

THE XAVIER INSTITUTE FOR HIGHER LEARNING
AVALANCHE, WAKE UP!
WE'RE SUPPOSED TA BE THE BROTHERHOOD OF MUTANTS! WE'RE SUPPOSED TA BE TOUGH!
WE CAN'T GET TAKEN OUT BY A GIRL, YA PANTY-WAIST MOOK!
SHAKOOM
I--I...
I THOUGHT YOU SAID WE WERE SAFE!
MINDEE, WHAT'S GOING ON?!
WELL, I LIED, OKAY? I JUST DIDN'T SEE THE NEED TO WORRY YOU.
I'M PROJECTING ALTERNATE IMAGES OF US INTO EXODUS'S MIND, BUT HE'LL FIND HIS TARGET SOON ENOUGH AND KILL US BOTH!
SHAKOOM
SHBOOOM
KOOM
IS...IS THIS WHAT IT FEELS LIKE TO LOSE?

HHNNNGGH!

AAH!
SORRY, MR. LeBEAU!
I'M NOT USED TO THESE DARING RESCUES!
AH, JAY, THE MUSIC-HATER.
WHERE ARE WE GOING?
I DON'T KNOW. SOMEPLACE SAFE AND FAR AWAY, IF I CAN MAKE IT.
NO. JUST CIRCLE AROUND THE MANSION...
...I MIGHT BE ABLE TO LATCH ONTO BLACK TOM'S MIND FROM UP HERE.
IT'S NO USE STRUGGLING, ROGUE. HANGING THIS WAY, YOU HAVE NO LEVERAGE.
AND YOU CAN'T ABSORB MY POWERS, BECAUSE MY MIND IS ELSEWHERE.
I'VE HELD JUGGERNAUT AT BAY LIKE THIS FOR HOURS. THERE'S NO WAY YOU COULD POSSIBLY WORK FREE.
SO JUST LIE BACK--RELAX--AND ENJOY YOUR LITTLE DEATH.

WELL, WELL...LOOK WHO'S HERE.
POLARIS AND HAVOK AND DOG-BREATH.
OTHERWISE KNOWN AS "DEAD MEAT."
AS LONG AS YOUR LUMPS DON'T GET MIXED UP WITH MINE--
--I'M GOOD WITH THAT.
PLEASE. WHEN HAVE YOU EVER BEEN A THREAT, VICTOR?
NEVER.
THE REST OF YOU, GO.
LOGAN, JUST LET LORNA--
NO.
ME AND SABRETOOTH. IT'S LONG PAST TIME WE ENDED THIS ONCE AND FOR ALL.
WHAT ARE WE GONNA END, RUNT?
WE COULD FIGHT TILL WE'RE JUST LUMPS'A MEAT ON THE GROUND AND IT STILL WOULDN'T END.

MAMMOMAX, WE NEED TO REGROUP. WE CAME IN WITH NO PLAN AND--
AND WHOSE FAULT IS THAT, EXODUS?!
THIS IS NO TIME FOR PETULANCE! THE X-MEN ARE RETURNING, AND WE--
I CAN'T BELIEVE HOW GRADE-SCHOOL THIS WHOLE OPERATION WAS!
I THOUGHT YOU WERE MAGNETO'S DISCIPLE, FOR THE LUVA PETE!
I THOUGHT YOU PEOPLE KNEW WHAT YOU WERE DOIN', BUT YOU'RE NOTHIN' BUT A BUNCHA STREET THUGS IN SPANDEX--
YOUR INSOLENCE WILL NOT BE TOLERATED, MAMMOMAX. ESPECIALLY NOW, WHEN THE X-MEN ARE CLOSING IN--
WE'RE NOT "CLOSING IN," DIPSTICK--
--WE'RE HERE!

NORTHSTAR! MAKE SURE THE CHILDREN ARE SAFE!
AND DON'T FORGET TO CHECK THE INFIRMARY!
I WANT TO MAKE SURE ANNIE AND CARTER ARE ALL RIGHT!
UH--YES. OF COURSE.
BUT I'M--EH--SURE THEY'RE FINE, ALEX. JUST FINE.
UFF!
I WANT BLACK TOM! NOT YOU, YOU LOSER!
OUTTA MY WAY!
THOOM

IT IS FUN KILLING EVERYONE!

HAVOK! WHAT'S OUR NEXT MOVE?
JUST KEEP FIGHTING!
THERE HAS TO BE A WAY TO STOP TOM!
EASY FOR YOU TO SAY!
WE NEED SOMEONE WHO CAN CONTROL MINDS!
I'VE BEEN TRYING! BUT THERE'S NO CENTRAL MIND TO CONTROL!
ARE WE OUT OF OPTIONS?!
MAYBE--

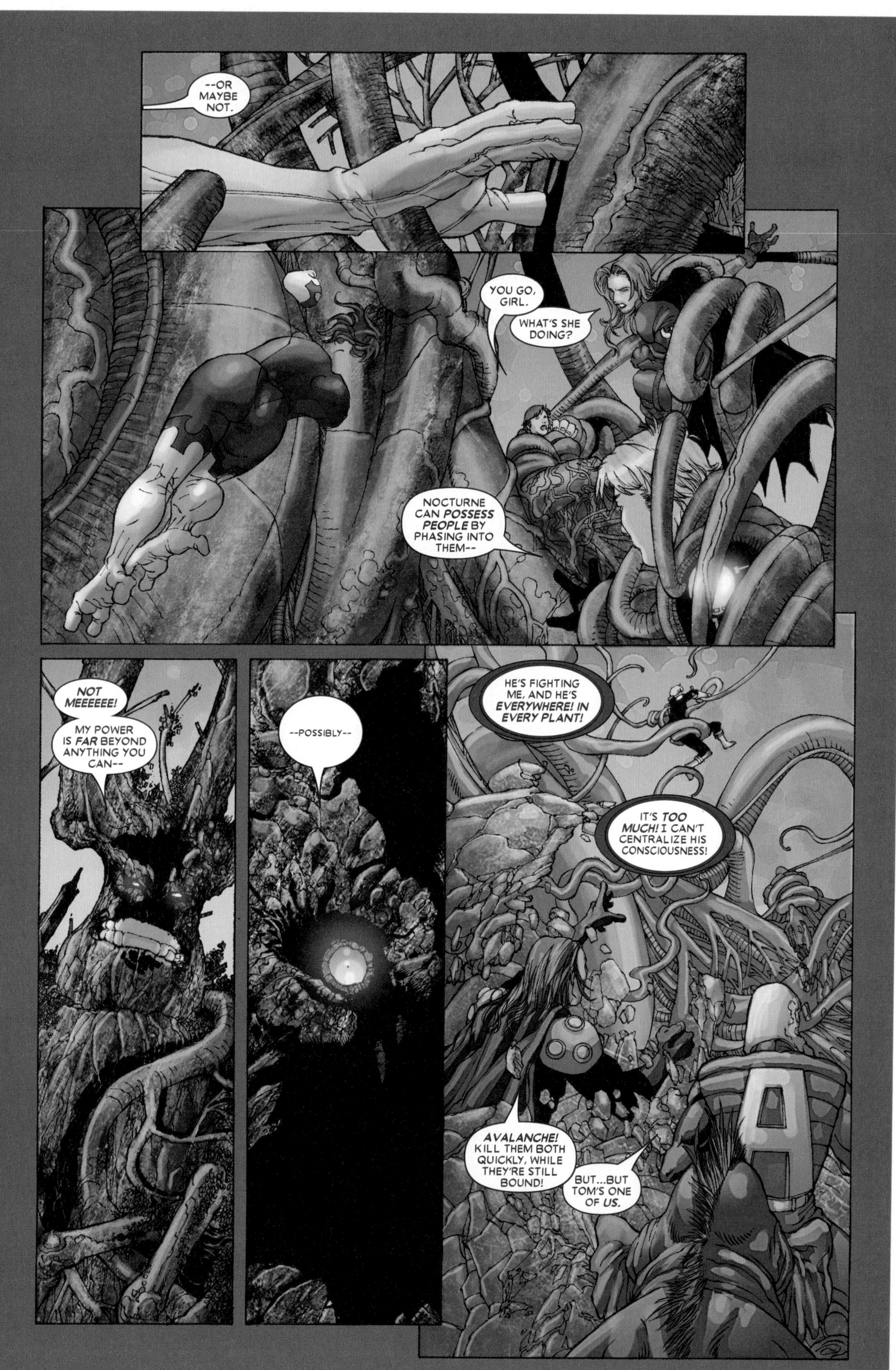
--OR MAYBE NOT.
YOU GO, GIRL.
WHAT'S SHE DOING?
NOCTURNE CAN POSSESS PEOPLE BY PHASING INTO THEM--
NOT MEEEEEE!
MY POWER IS FAR BEYOND ANYTHING YOU CAN--
--POSSIBLY--
HE'S FIGHTING ME, AND HE'S EVERYWHERE! IN EVERY PLANT!
IT'S TOO MUCH! I CAN'T CENTRALIZE HIS CONSCIOUSNESS!
AVALANCHE! KILL THEM BOTH QUICKLY, WHILE THEY'RE STILL BOUND!
BUT...BUT TOM'S ONE OF US.

NO ONE'S DYING WHILE I'M HERE!
POLARIS, MOVE THE X-MEN TO SAFETY-- QUICKLY.
WHAT?
XORN, WHY?
BECAUSE I HAVE DECIDED I CANNOT ALLOW ANY MORE INNOCENTS TO DIE.
ONCE MORE I AM OPENING THE BLACK HOLE THAT IS MY MIND.
BUT YOU DON'T KNOW WHERE THEY GO WHEN THEY GET SUCKED INTO THAT HEAD OF YOURS!
SUPPOSE IT'S SOMEPLACE THEY CAN COME BACK FROM?! THE SCHOOL WILL NEVER BE SAFE!
IT WILL IF THEY DON'T REMEMBER WHERE WE ARE! LET ME ATTEMPT A MIND-WIPE!
UNFORTUNATELY, I MAY AFFECT NOCTURNE'S MIND AS I WIPE BLACK TOM'S MEMORY!
THAT'S A RISKY MOVE, GIRL! WHAT IF NOCTURNE GETS PULLED INTO XORN WITH ALL THE OTHERS?
SO DO IT! IT'S THE ONLY WAY!
I CAN'T HOLD TOM MUCH LONGER...AND I DOUBT YOU CAN STOP HIM ONCE I'VE LOST CONTROL! HE'S TOO POWERFUL!
XORN, WE HAVE TO FIND ANOTHER WAY!
THERE IS NO OTHER WAY, LORNA. I SENSE THAT THIS IS A TURNING POINT FOR ME--FOR ALL OF US.

WE ALL KNEW THE JOB WAS DANGEROUS WHEN WE *TOOK IT*, POLARIS!
IT'S PART OF THE *HERO TERRITORY!*
I'VE WIPED THE ELEPHANT'S MIND! GET TO SAFETY NOW, JUGGERNAUT!
NAH, *YOU ALL* GET TO SAFETY. I THINK I'LL TAKE THIS RIDE--
--AND LOOK OUT FOR *NOCTURNE*--
--IF WE *SURVIVE.*
THEN MAYBE I'LL GET TO SEE *SAMMY* AGAIN--
AND IF YOU DON'T?!
--AND SHOW HIM *I'M* A HERO, TOO.
AAAAHHH--

CAIN...
BE GOOD, BOSS MAN.
SSSSHHHHHHHHH
SSSSSSSSSSS

FWOOOOMF
I...I'M GETTING NO MENTAL RESIDUE OF BLACK TOM.
OR JUGGERNAUT, OR NOCTURNE...
...OR ANYONE ELSE.
XORN? ARE--ARE YOU ALL RIGHT?
NO, ALEX. I AM NOT ALL RIGHT. I...I AM NOT SURE WHAT HAPPENED TO ALL OF THOSE PEOPLE.
I WILL NEED SOME TIME ALONE, AWAY FROM HERE, TO MEDITATE ON THE IMMENSITY OF MY ACTIONS.
IF IT IS ACCEPTABLE TO YOU THAT I LEAVE HERE, THAT IS.
O-OF COURSE, XORN. WHATEVER YOU NEED.
BUT WAIT A MINUTE. WHERE DID THEY GO?
ARE THEY DEAD? CAN WE GET THEM BACK?
ALEX...CAIN, NOCTURNE? HOW WILL WE GET THEM BACK?
I DON'T KNOW, JEAN-PAUL.
BUT WE'LL DO ALL THAT WE CAN.

AND WHAT DO YOU INTEND TO DO NOW?
I INTEND TO MAKE SURE WOLVERINE HAS DEALT WITH THE LAST OF THE NEW AND NOT-SO-IMPROVED BROTHERHOOD.
LOGAN?
HE'S ALIVE!
YEAH.
SURPRISED EVEN ME.
WHERE'S SABRETOOTH?
SORT OF SPREAD AROUND, HERE...
...LET'S JUST SAY HE'S FEEDIN' THE PLANTS, AND LEAVE IT AT THAT.
END